JOHN THOMPSON'S
EASIEST PIANO COUR

C000109169

FIRST CHILDREN'S SONGS

This collection of children's songs is intended as supplementary material for those working through **John Thompson's Easiest Piano Course** Parts 2–4. The pieces may also be used for sight reading practice by more advanced students.

Dynamics and phrasing have been deliberately omitted from the earlier pieces, since they are not introduced until Part 3 of the Easiest Piano Course, and initially the student's attention should be focused on playing notes and rhythms accurately. Outline fingering has been included, and in general the hand is assumed to remain in a five-finger position until a new fingering indicates a position shift. The fingering should suit most hands, although logical alternatives are always possible.

Twinkle, Twinkle, Little Star

Traditional

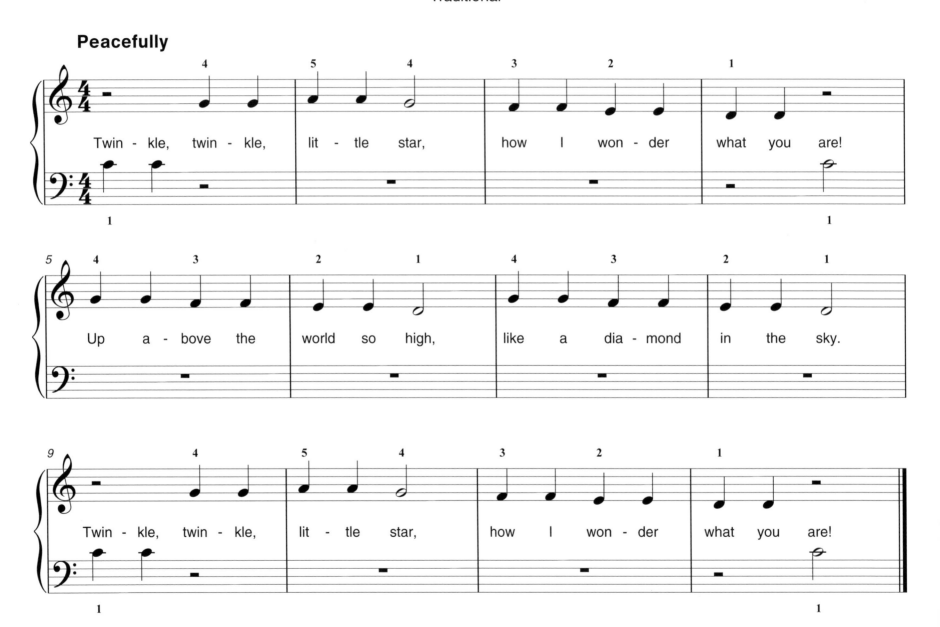

The Wheels On The Bus

Traditional

Briskly

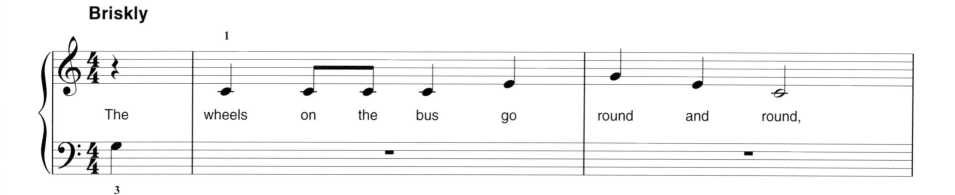

The wheels on the bus go round and round,

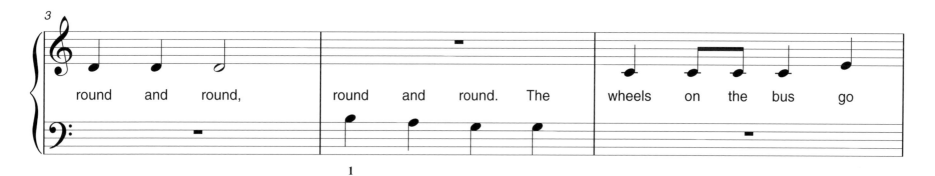

round and round, round and round. The wheels on the bus go

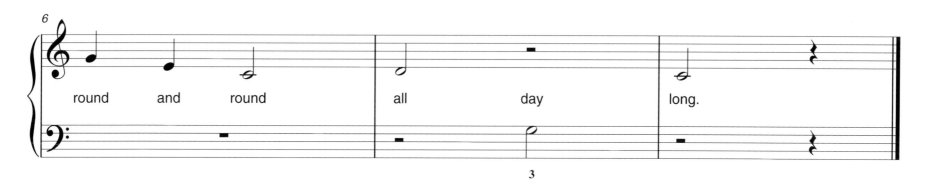

round and round all day long.

Baa, Baa, Black Sheep

Traditional

Smoothly

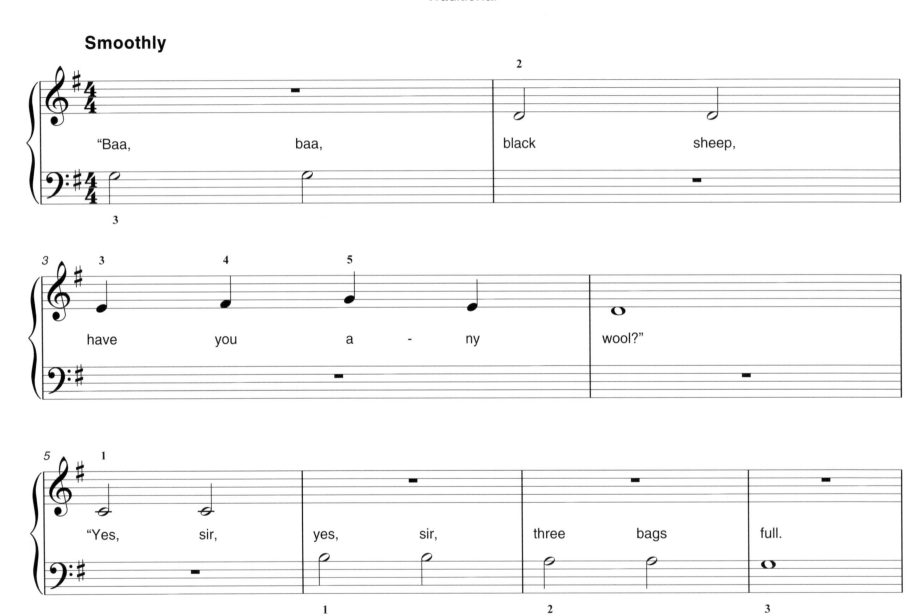

One for my mas - - ter and

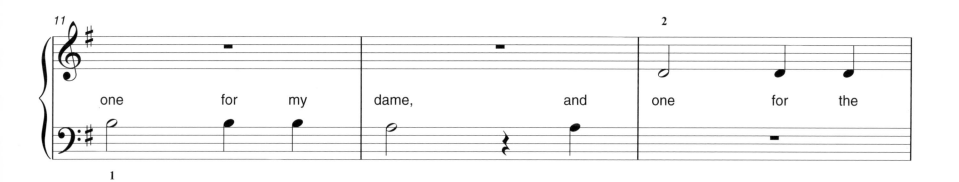

one for my dame, and one for the

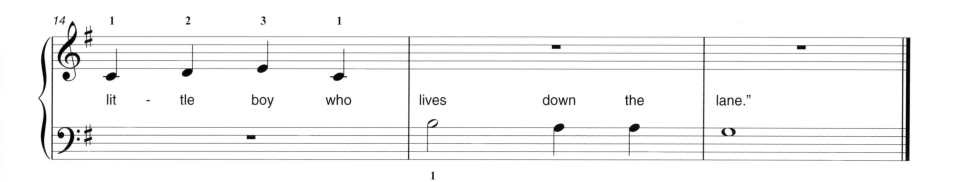

lit - tle boy who lives down the lane."

5

She'll Be Coming 'Round The Mountain

Traditional

Spiritedly

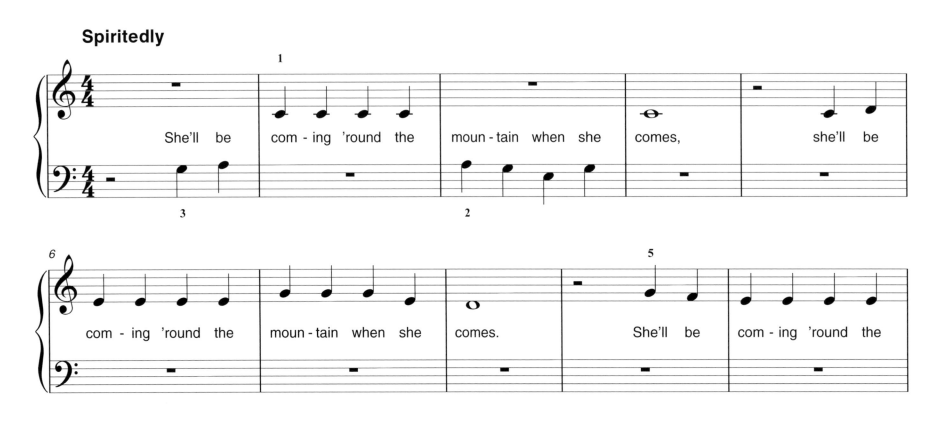

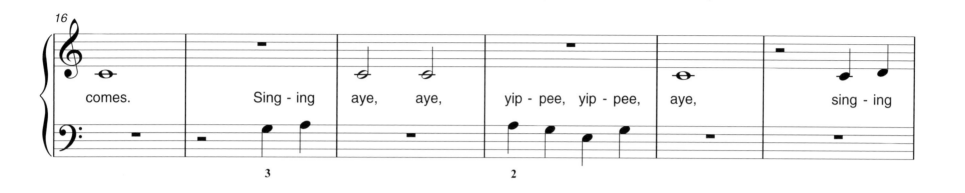

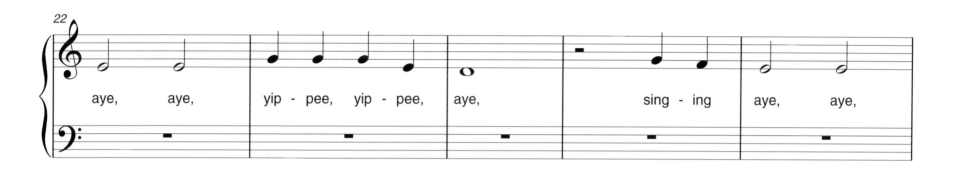

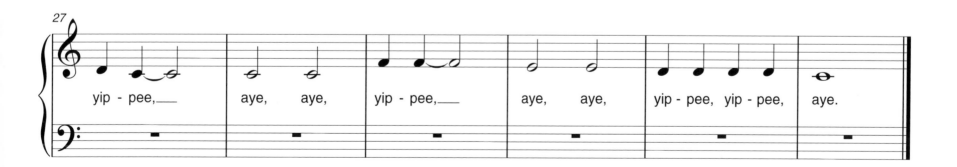

A-tisket, A-tasket

Traditional

Crisply

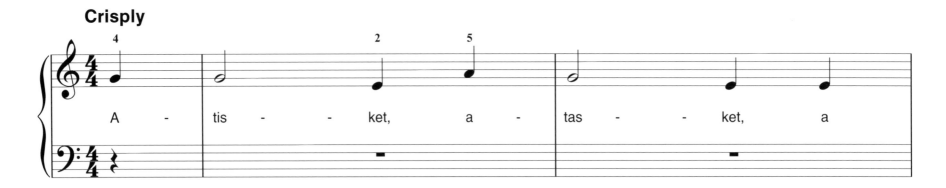

A - tis - ket, a - tas - ket, a

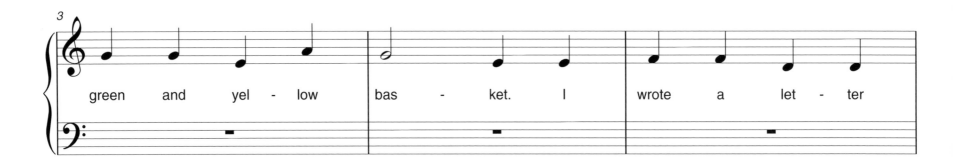

green and yel - low bas - ket. I wrote a let - ter

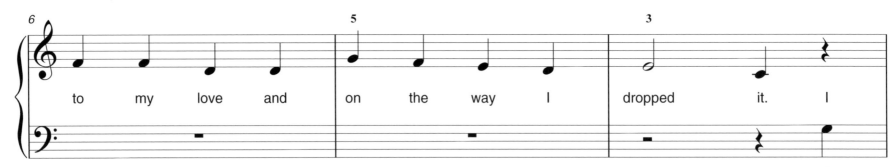

to my love and on the way I dropped it. I

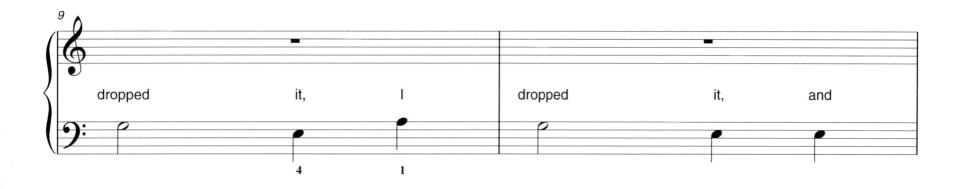

dropped   it,   I   dropped   it,   and

on   the   way   I   dropped   it.   A   lit - tle   girl - ie

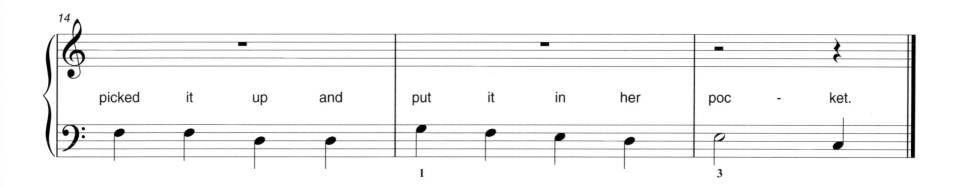

picked   it   up   and   put   it   in   her   poc - ket.

Michael Finnegan

Traditional

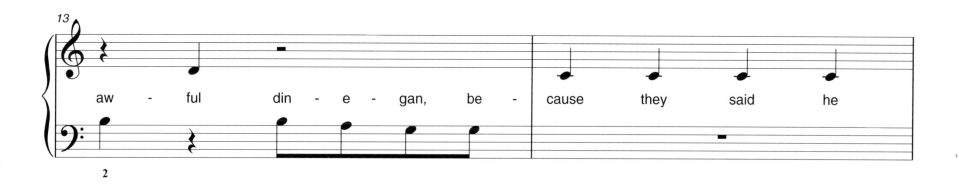

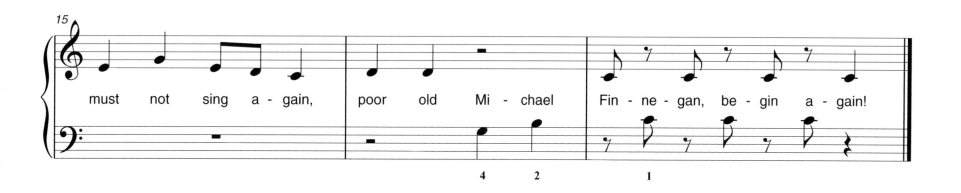

Three Blind Mice

Traditional

12

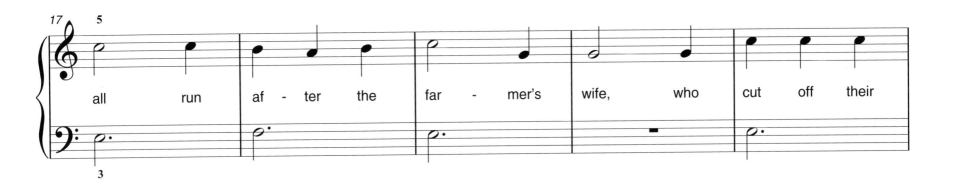

all run af - ter the far - mer's wife, who cut off their

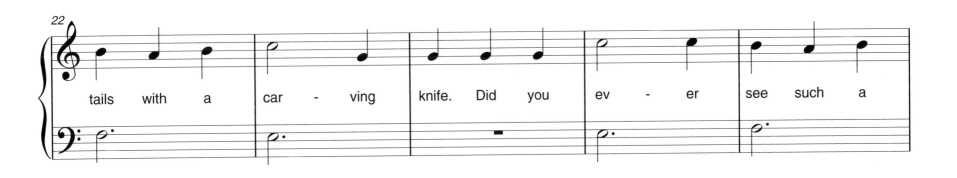

tails with a car - ving knife. Did you ev - er see such a

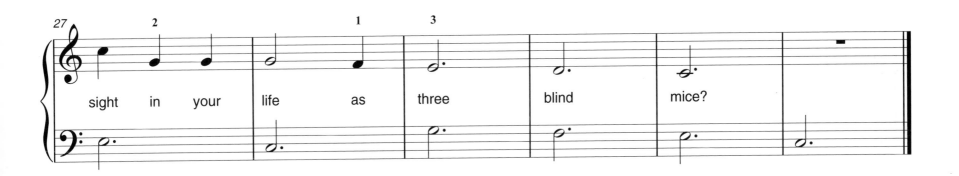

sight in your life as three blind mice?

Polly, Put The Kettle On

Traditional

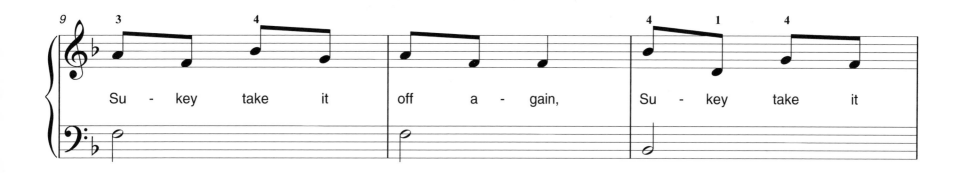

Su - key take it off a - gain, Su - key take it

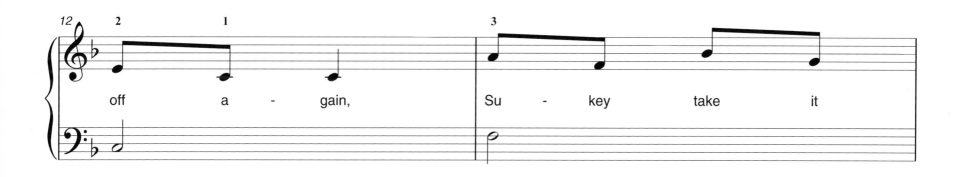

off a - gain, Su - key take it

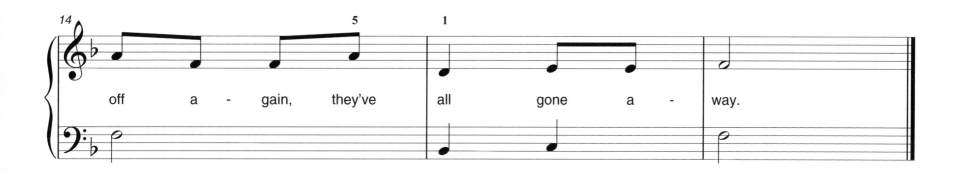

off a - gain, they've all gone a - way.

Old MacDonald Had A Farm

Traditional

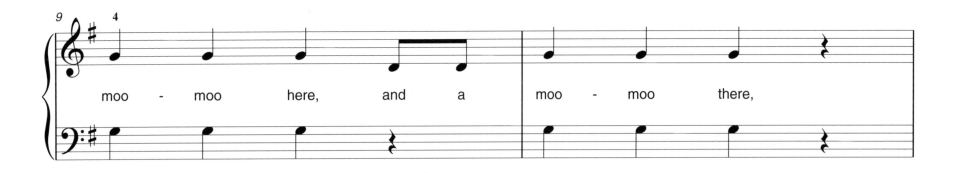

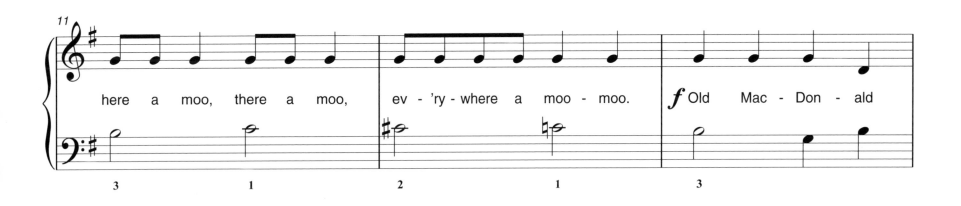

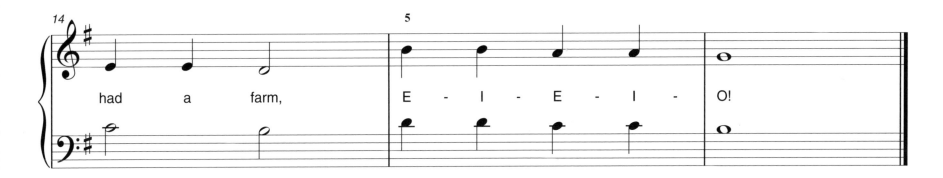

The Muffin Man

Traditional

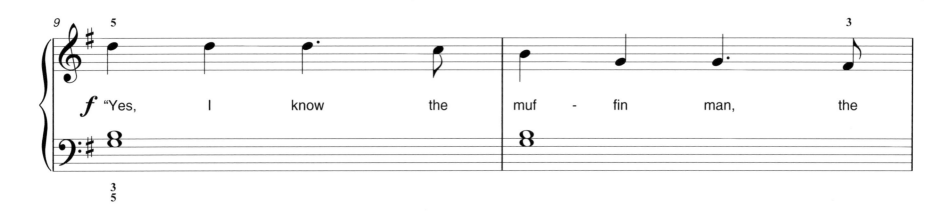

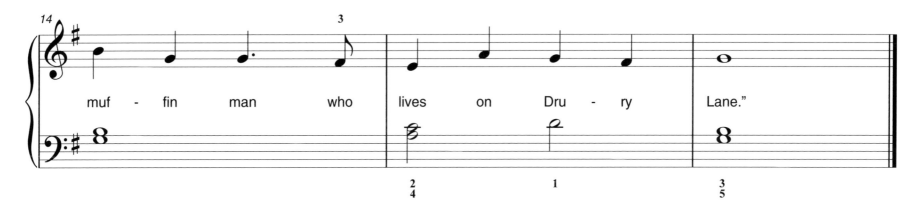

Row, Row, Row Your Boat

Traditional

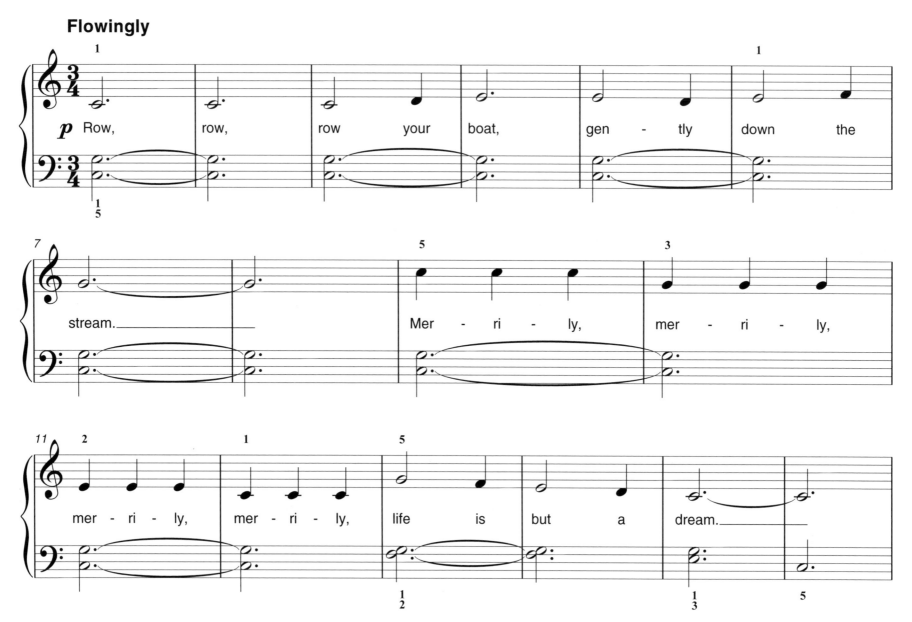

Flowingly

p Row, row, row your boat, gen - tly down the stream.

Mer - ri - ly, mer - ri - ly, mer - ri - ly, mer - ri - ly, life is but a dream.

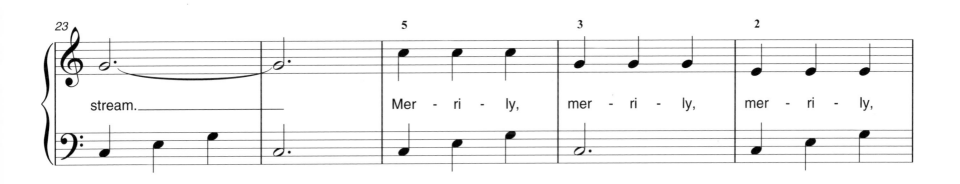

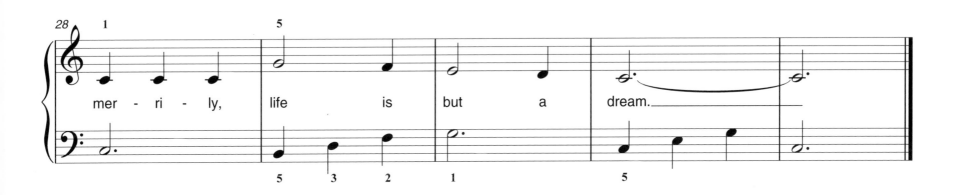

Polly Wolly Doodle

Traditional

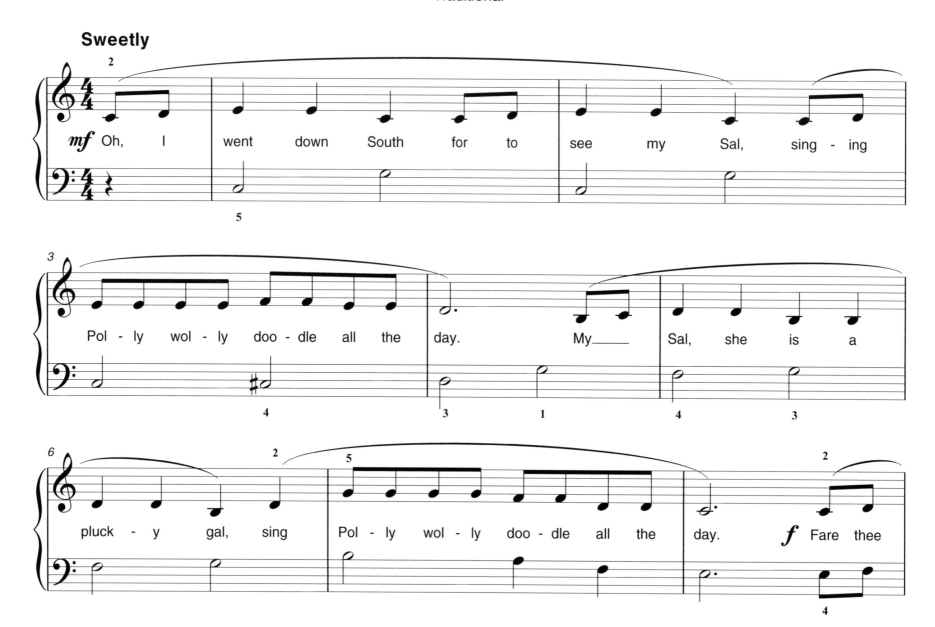

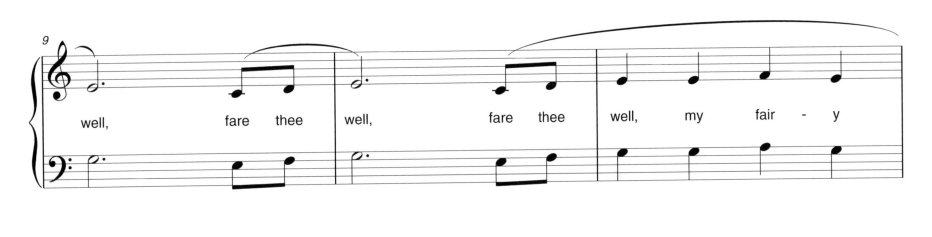

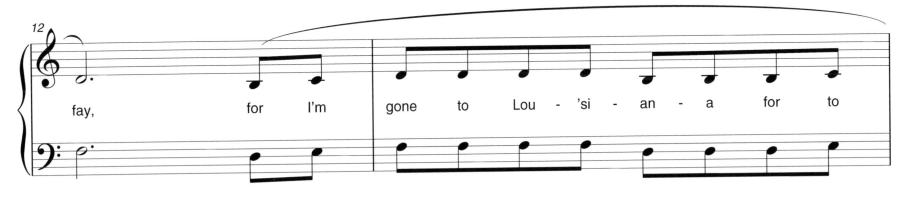

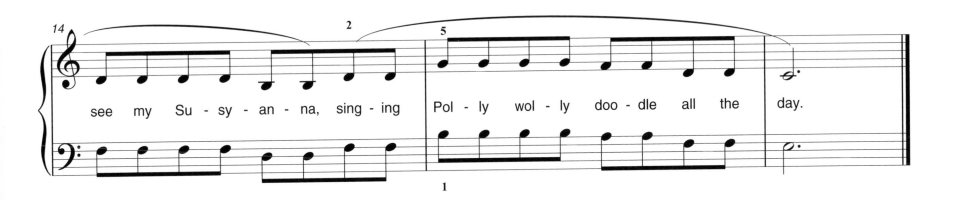

23

Alice The Camel

Traditional

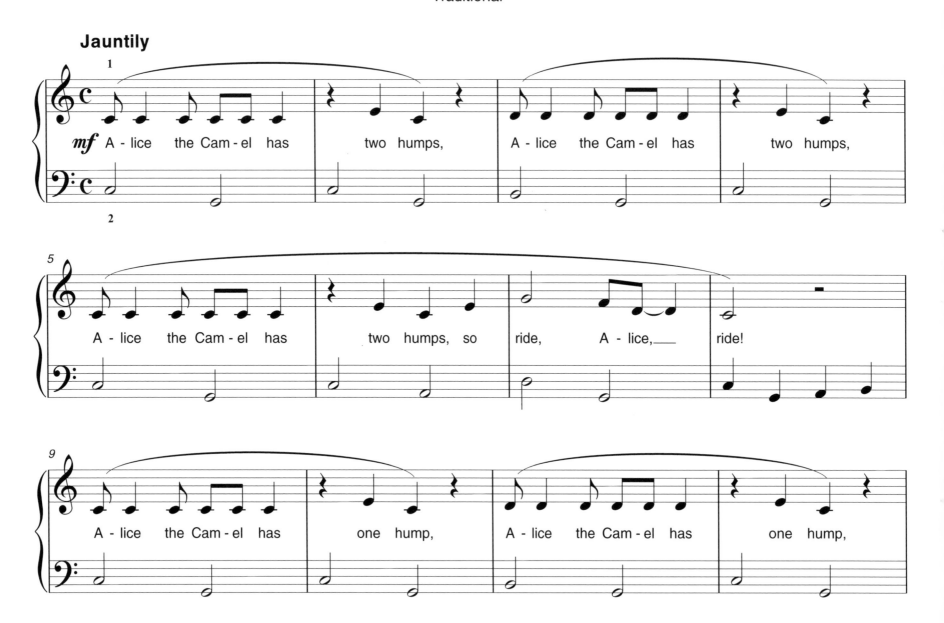

A - lice the Cam - el has one hump, so ride, A - lice,___ ride!

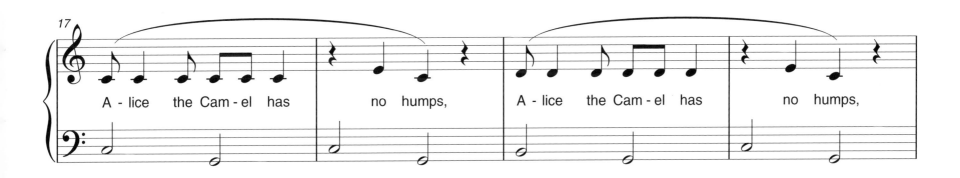

A - lice the Cam - el has no humps, A - lice the Cam - el has no humps,

rit.

A - lice the Cam - el has no humps, 'cause A - lice___ is a___ horse!

25

Pop! Goes The Weasel

Traditional

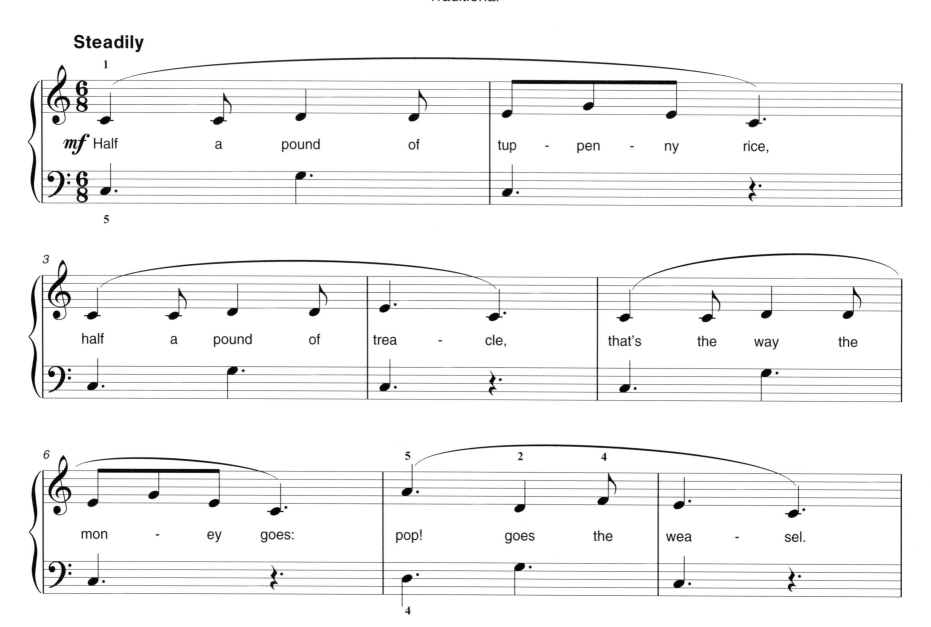

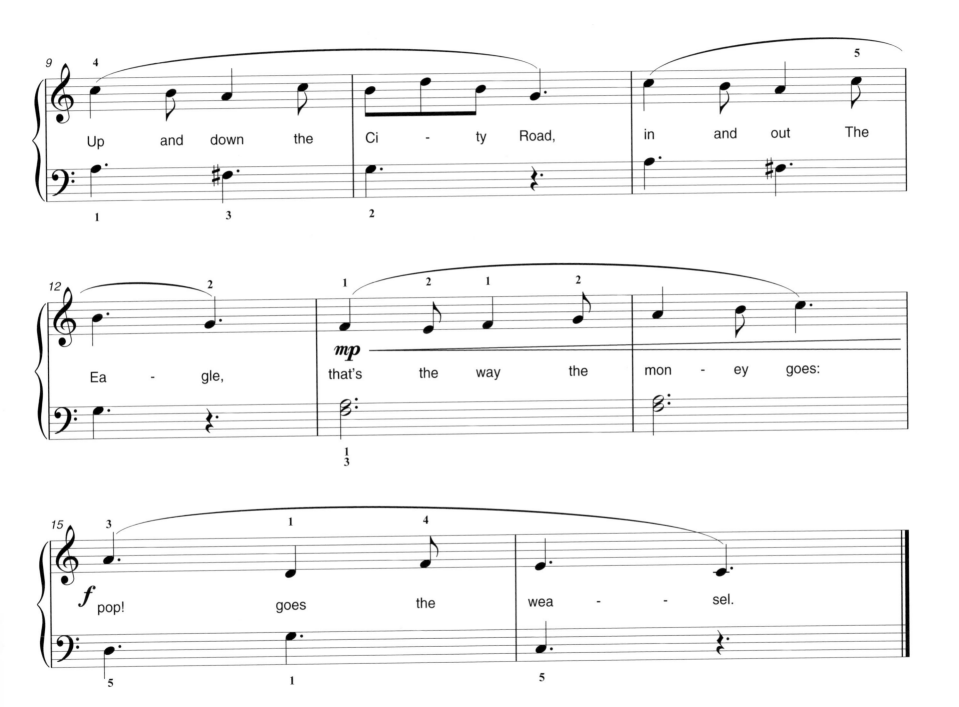

Up and down the Ci - ty Road, in and out The

Ea - gle, that's the way the mon - ey goes:

pop! goes the wea - sel.

The Animal Fair

Traditional

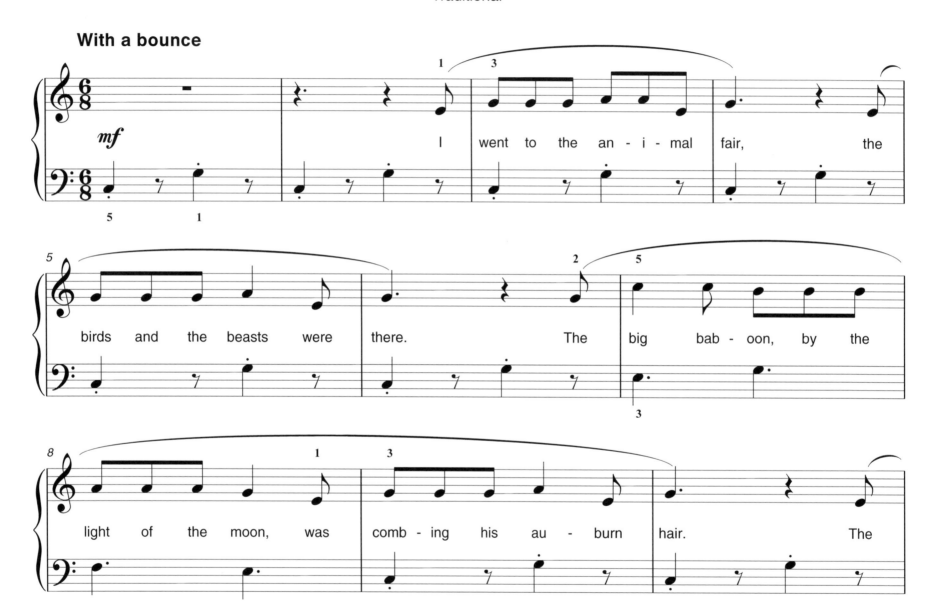

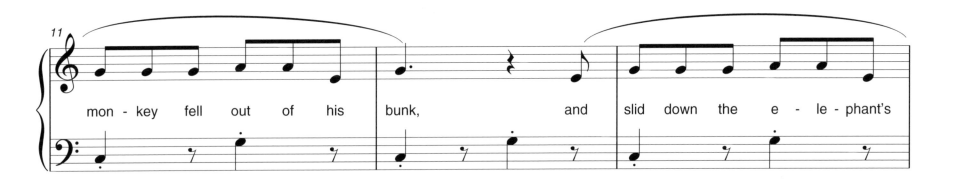

mon - key fell out of his bunk, and slid down the e - le - phant's

trunk. The e - le - phant sneezed and fell on her knees, and what be - came of the

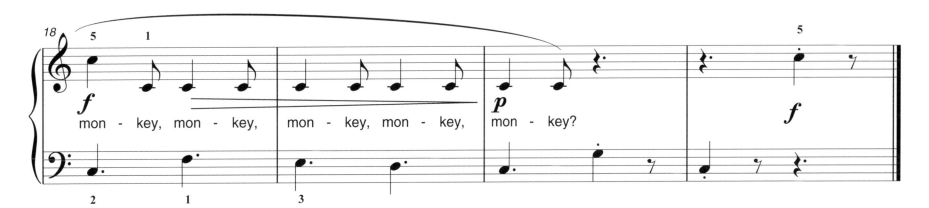

mon - key, mon - key, mon - key, mon - key, mon - key?

Happy Birthday To You

Words & Music by Patty S. Hill & Mildred Hill

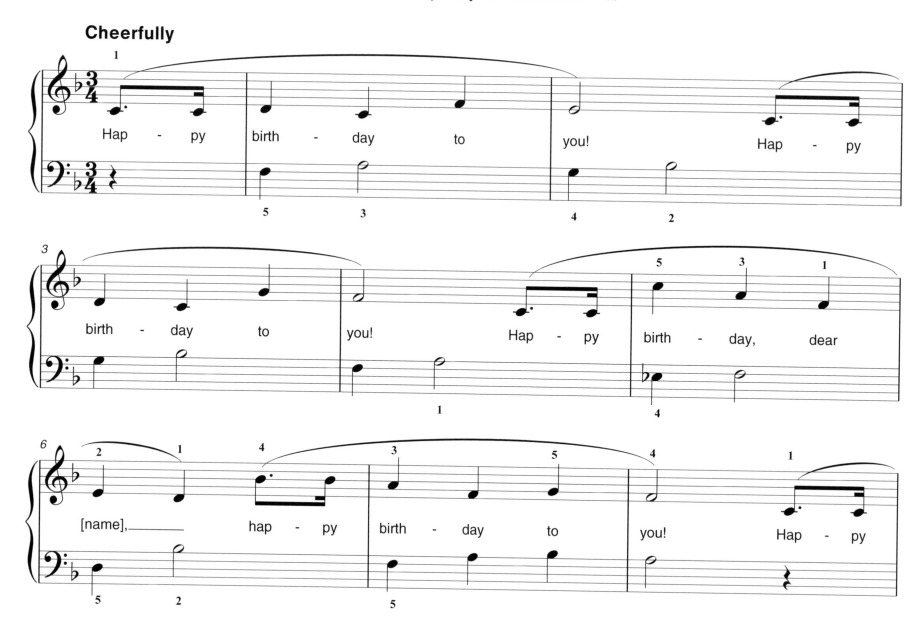

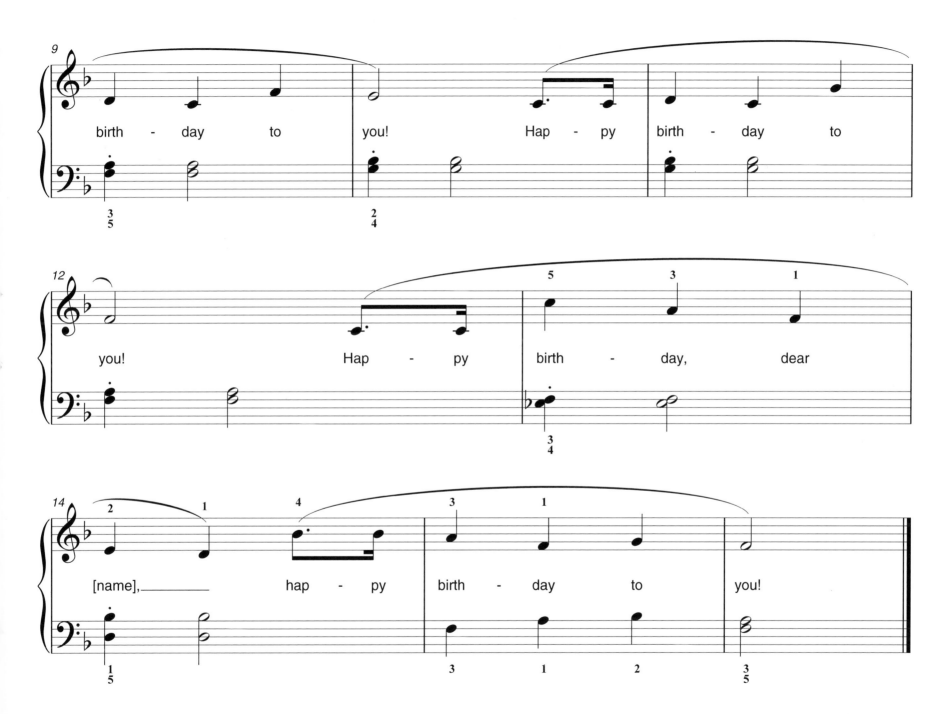

© Copyright 2017 The Willis Music Company
Florence, Kentucky, USA. All Rights Reserved.

Exclusive Distributors:
Music Sales Limited
Newmarket Road, Bury St Edmunds, Suffolk IP33 3YB, UK.

Order No. WMR101816
ISBN: 978-1-78558-528-9

Arranged by Christopher Hussey.
Arrangements and engravings supplied by Camden Music Services.
Cover illustration by Sergio Sandoval.

Printed in the EU.